Michael Jacques

C000192835

sounds good!

Recorder or Flute

Five pieces for descant or treble recorder
or flute with piano accompaniment

ABRSM

Published by ABRSM (Publishing) Ltd, a wholly owned subsidiary of ABRSM

SOUNDS GOOD!

1
Hop, Skip and Jump

MICHAEL JACQUES

AB 2303

SOUNDS GOOD!

1
Hop, Skip and Jump

Descant Recorder

MICHAEL JACQUES

AB 2303

2
Sleepy Waltz

With gentle movement (♩ = 66)

3
Best Foot Forward

With a jaunty swing (♩ = 132)

4
Film Theme

Warm and expressive (♩ = 76)

5
Fiesta

SOUNDS GOOD!

1
Hop, Skip and Jump

Flute (or Treble Recorder)

MICHAEL JACQUES

AB 2303

Flute (or Treble Recorder)

2
Sleepy Waltz

With gentle movement (♩ = 66)

3
Best Foot Forward

With a jaunty swing (♩ = 132)

4
Film Theme

5
Fiesta

Carefree and rhythmic (♩. = 88)

4

2
Sleepy Waltz

With gentle movement (♩ = 66)

3
Best Foot Forward

4
Film Theme

Warm and expressive (♩ = 76)

5
Fiesta

Carefree and rhythmic (♩. = 88)

14

Printed in England by Caligraving Limited Thetford Norfolk   AB 2303